DILBERT DILBERT DILBERT DILBERT
DILBERT DILBERT DILBERT DILBERT D
BERT DILBERT DILBERT DILBERT
RT DILBERT DILBERT
RT DILBERT DILBERT
BERT DILBERT
ILBERT
BERT D
LBE
RT DI
RT DI
ILBERT DILBERT
BERT DILBERT DILBERT
DILBERT DILBERT DILBERT DILBERT D
DILBERT DILBERT DILBERT DILBERT
DILBERT DILBERT DILBERT
LBERT DILBERT DILBERT DILBERT DI
BERT DILBERT DILBERT DILBERT DILBERT
LBERT DILBERT DILBERT DILBERT DILBERT
ILBERT DILBERT DILBERT DILBERT
RT DILBERT DILBERT DILBERT DILBERT DI
BERT DILBERT DILBERT DILBERT DILBERT
RT DILBERT DILBERT

COMMUNICATION IS GOOD!

FOR _____

FROM _____

TELLING IT LIKE IT ISN'T.

A DILBERT™ BOOK
BY
SCOTT ADAMS

B⬟XTREE

First published in 1996 by Andrews and McMeel, a Universal Press Syndicate Company,
4900 Main Street, Kansas City, Missouri, 64112, USA

This edition published in 1997 by Boxtree,
an imprint of Macmillan Publishers Ltd,
25 Eccleston Place, London, SW1W 9NF
and Basingstoke

Associated companies throughout the world

ISBN 0 7522 2426 3

3 5 7 9 8 6 4 2

A CIP catalogue record for this book is available from the British Library

Printed in Singapore

TELLING IT LIKE
IT ISN'T

I'M SO LUCKY TO BE DATING YOU, LIZ. YOU'RE AT LEAST AN EIGHT.
YOU'RE A TEN.

ARE WE USING THE SAME SCALE?
TEN IS THE NUMBER OF SECONDS IT WOULD TAKE TO REPLACE YOU.

TODAY WE HAVE A MOTIVATIONAL SPEAKER FROM THE "DISCOUNT SPEAKERS BUREAU."

YOU SHOULD, LIKE, WORK HARDER...OTHERWIS YOU MIGHT GET FIRED. ANY QUESTIONS?

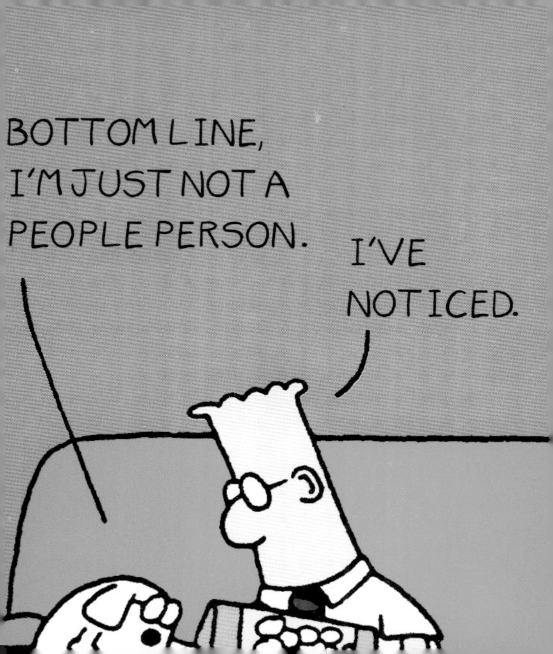
BOTTOM LINE, I'M JUST NOT A PEOPLE PERSON.
I'VE NOTICED.

I DIDN'T KNOW YOU
WERE THE DIRECTOR OF
PRODUCT ENHANCEMENTS.

I'M NEVER GOING BACK. I CAN'T. I WON'T.
MY BLOUSE FALLS TO THE FLOOR...
BREAK! BREAK!

LET'S GO AROUND THE TABLE AND GIVE AN UPDATE ON EACH OF OUR PROJECTS.

MY PROJECT IS A PATHETIC SERIES OF POORLY PLANNED, NEAR-RANDOM ACTS. MY LIFE IS A TRAGEDY OF EMOTIONAL DESPERATION.

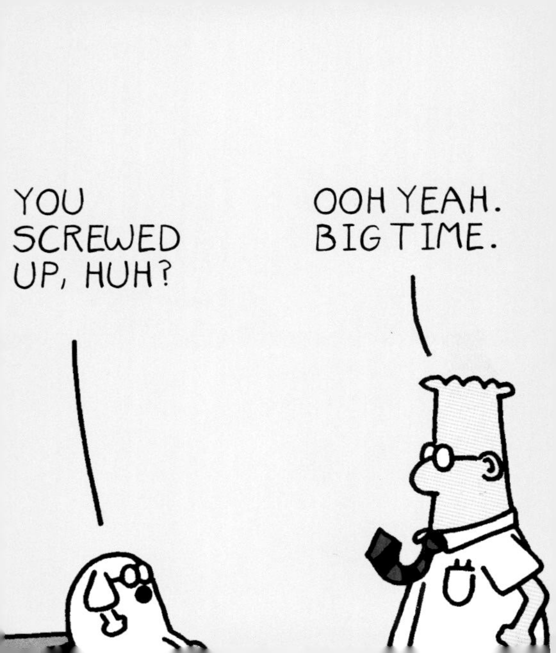
YOU SCREWED UP, HUH?
OOH YEAH. BIG TIME.

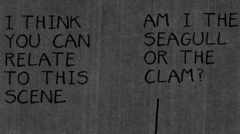

OH,
THAT
REMINDS ME:
YOU'RE FIRED.

STICK TO THE SCRIPT. ACT SINCERE AND BEG YOUR CUSTOMERS TO FORGIVE YOU.

IT WAS WRONG FOR US TO SELL KEYBOARDS WITH NO "Q." WE'RE SORRY. WE'RE MORONS.

WE'RE DUMBER THAN SQUIRRELS. WE HEAR VOICES AND DO WHAT THEY COMMAND. I HAVE BROCCOLI IN MY SOCKS.
GOOD WRITING.
THANKS

... FORTUNATELY I CONVINCED HIM TO TAKE MY LASER PRINTER INSTEAD...
WHAT DID I SAY THAT SOUNDED LIKE "TELL ME ABOUT YOUR DAY"?

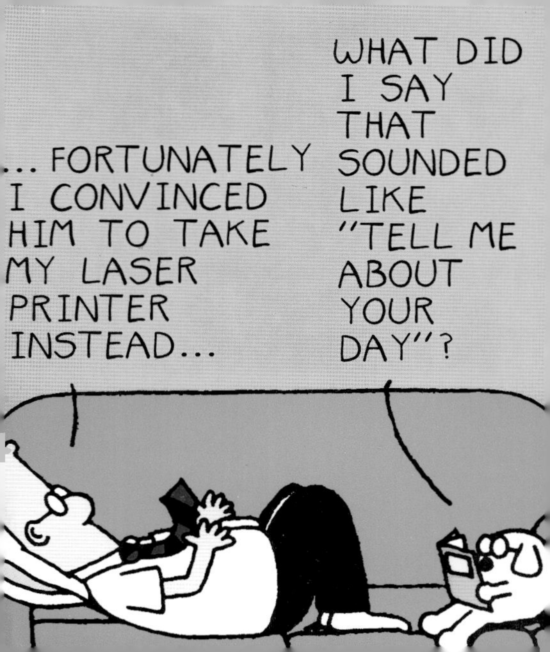